SPACE ENCYCLOPEDIA

STARS

Om
KIDZ
An imprint of Om Books International

Contents

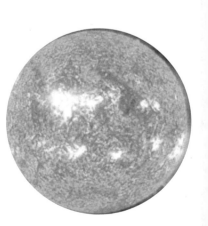

STARS

▲ *An artist's representation of the stars and constellations in a clear sky at twilight.*

Stars are described as large, hot and flaming balls of gas. The star most familiar to us is the Sun. However, stars are not really made up of gas. They are massive, luminous spheres of plasma.

They are held together due to their own gravity, which gives them their characteristic spherical shape. The sphere minimises the area of the star's surface to a given mass.

Thus, it is the most efficient way for gravity to arrange the star's mass.

They originate with the gravitational collapse of a gaseous nebula. They are primarily composed of hydrogen, along with helium and trace amounts of heavier elements.

Life Cycle of a Star

Stars are born from a nebula. Huge clouds of dust and gas collapse under gravitational forces, forming proto-stars. These young stars undergo a further collapse, forming main sequence stars. They expand as they grow old. As the core exhausts its hydrogen and then helium, it contracts and the outer layers expand, cool and become less bright. This is a red giant or a red super giant, depending on the initial mass of the star. It will finally collapse and explode. Depending on the original mass of the star, it will either become a black dwarf, neutron star or black hole.

Stages that every star undergoes.

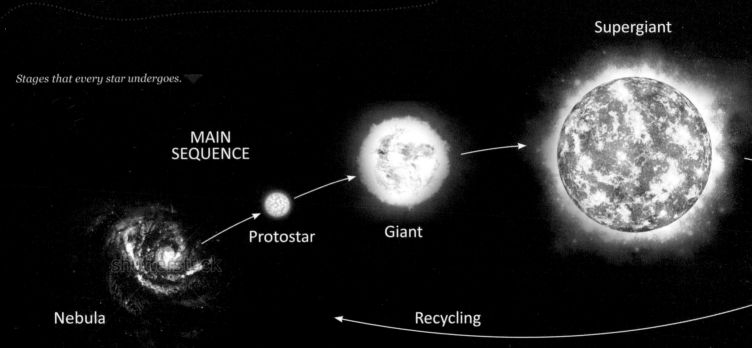

MAIN SEQUENCE

Protostar

Giant

Supergiant

Nebula

Recycling

Nebulae and proto stars

Spaces between stars are not empty but filled with gas and dust called interstellar matter. This matter clumps together to form clouds. It is in these clouds or nebula that stars are born. Certain events cause a nebula to collapse under its own gravity. As it continues to collapse the temperature increases. The hot core at the centre eventually forms a protostar. As the temperature and pressure further increases, it starts releasing energy, becomes luminous and forms a main sequence star.

Main sequence stars

All stars pass through the main sequence stage. The majority spend their lives as main sequence stars. They come in a variety of masses, sizes, colours and luminosity.

The sun is a main sequence star. Hydrogen is converted into helium in the centre through nuclear fusion. Light and heat energy are produced during this process that has been occurring for more than 4.5 billion years. As it matures, it will move into a new stage. This will lead to a change in its appearance .

Giants and supergiants

After a star leaves the main sequence, its core contracts and heats up. Burning hydrogen ignites in a shell around the centre, causing the envelope to expand, but as it does, it cools. The cooler, but bigger star becomes redder and more luminous. Eventually, the temperature at the core reaches 100 million degrees and burning helium ignites in the core. The star, at this point, has a surface temperature of about 3200 °C and a radius equal to Mercury's orbit. It has now transformed into a red giant.

The cat's eye nebula is so called because the intersection of the two halos formed by the nebula looks like a cat's eye. Astronomers suspect that this is a twin star.

Type II
Supernova

Supernova
Remnant

Neutron
Star

Black Hole

The ant nebula

Ant Nebula, also known as Menzel 3, or Mz 3, is a young bipolar planetary nebula about two light years in diameter, which is radially expanding at a rate of about 50 km per second.
It is located some 8000 light years away in the constellation Norma. It gets its name because it resembles the head and thorax of an ant.

Cat's eye nebula

Three thousand light years away, the Cat's eye nebula is a dying star that throws off shells of glowing gas. Research reveals that this nebula is one of the most complex planetary nebulae known. In fact, the features seen here are so complex that it leads astronomers to suspect that the bright central object may in fact be a binary star system.

Red rectangle nebula

The Red Rectangle Nebula, also known as HD 44179, is so called because of its red colour and unique rectangular shape. It is a bipolar, proto-planetary nebula, which is located about 2,300 light years away towards the constellation Monoceros. Protoplanetary nebulas are formed by old stars, which are in the process of becoming planetary nebulae. In a few thousand years, once the expulsion of mass is complete, a very hot, white dwarf star will remain and its luminous ultraviolet radiation will cause the surrounding gas to glow.

White dwarfs

The path followed from a red giant depends on the mass of a star. Stars like the Sun are small and pass through the planetary nebula phase. The outer layers drift away and the core is very hot, shines brightly and becomes what is called white dwarf stars . They contain highly compressed carbon and oxygen materials. With time they cool down further, stop shining and form cold black dwarfs. .

Supernova and black holes.

The violent explosion that occurs when a high-mass star comes to an end is called a supernova. When all the dust moves away what remains behind of the compact core is a dense star called the neutron star. When neutron stars begin to spin rapidly they are called pulsars. When an exploding star is extremely large it could form what is called a black hole. Although we cannot see anything in the region of a black hole, we can see the effects on the stars and other bodies around it.

Star Quality

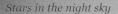
There are billions of stars, including the Sun, in the Milky Way. Quiet interestingly, there are billions of galaxies in the universe. So far, we have learned that hundreds of stars also have planets orbiting them. Since the beginning of civilisation, stars have played a significant role in religion and have proven to be crucial to navigation. Astronomy, the study of the heavens, may be the most ancient of the sciences.

1. Colour and temperature

A star's colour is determined by its temperature. Its colour keeps changing with changes in its temperature. An early schema from the 19th century ranked stars from A to P. After several transformations, the classification includes seven main types today: O, B, A, F, G, K and M. Blue stars range from 5,000-28,000 K, blue-white stars 28,000–10,000 K, white stars 10,000–7,500 K, yellow-white stars 7,500– 6,000 K, yellow stars 6,000–4,900 K, orange stars 4,900–3,500 K and red stars 3,500–2,000 K.

2. Gravity and pressure

A star's gravity pulls the star's gas towards its centre. Simultaneously, the pressure of the dense core pushes out the material. The two forces balance each other, maintaining the star's size. Most of the stars are almost spherical, though the rapid spinning makes them bulge around the equator. When two stars are in close proximity, their shapes are distorted due to gravity pulling one to the other.

Stars in the night sky

3. Luminosity

Luminosity is the total amount of energy that is emitted by a star, galaxy or other astronomical object. It is related to the brightness of an object in a given spectral region. The most luminous stars emit more than six million times the Sun's light and the least luminous ones emit less than one ten-thousandth of it. It is an indication of a star's actual brightness as viewed from Earth. If the Sun was at a further distance, it would be dimmer, although it would still have the same luminosity.

4. Star size

Stars come in different sizes. The smallest stars, also called M-type stars or M stars are massive enough to initiate nuclear fusion in their core. If they were smaller, they would be brown dwarfs, yet many times bigger than the biggest planet in our solar system, Jupiter. The smallest stars out there are the tiny red dwarfs. These are stars with not more than 50 per cent of the mass of the Sun and they can have as little as 7.5 per cent its mass. This is the minimum mass required for a star to be able to support nuclear fusion in its core. The blue supergiant Rigel, in the constellation Orion, is an example of a star larger than the Sun. It is estimated to be 62 times as big as the Sun. Rigel's mass is 17 times that of the Sun, giving out 66,000 times as much energy.

Rigel, the star larger than our Sun.

5. Rotation

Stars rotate around themselves at a high speed. The younger they are, the faster they spin. The B-class star Acherner spins as fast as 225 km per second. This is very close to 300 km per second when a star will disintegrate as its mass will get flung outwards in all directions. The Acherner gets its shape because of its high rotation. Its equator has been pushed outwards and is twice the size of its circumference around the poles. The Sun also rotates, however, at a stable rate of about 2 km per second.

Black Holes

We've seen that medium stars die off by fading into black dwarfs, and giants and supergiants explode into supernovas. But it is interesting to know that this explosion doesn't really dissipate all the matter of the star. In fact, while most of the mass of the star is blown away, the rest forms a core. Depending on the size of the core, it behaves differently.

Pre-conditions for black holes

Most giants form a neutron star that manifests as a pulsar or X-ray burster. The largest stars, however, can leave a core larger than four times the mass of the Sun. These form black holes. A black hole is mathematically defined as a region of space so dense that nothing can escape its gravitational field.

Origin of theory

The idea of black holes was proposed in the theory of relativity written by Einstein. This theory predicts that a sufficiently compact mass will distort space-time to form a black hole. However, the idea originated when John Michell first put the idea of a body so massive that even light could not escape, in a letter written to Henry Cavendish in 1783.

He quoted, "If the semi-diameter of a sphere of the same density as the Sun were to exceed that of the Sun in the proportion of 500 to one, a body falling from an infinite height towards it would have acquired at its surface greater velocity than that of light, and consequently supposing light to be attracted by the same force in proportion to its visinertiae, with other bodies, all light emitted from such a body would be made to return towards it by its own proper gravity".

An artist's impression of an accretion disc. An accretion disc is formed due to the heating of matter as it enters the black hole and would be a very bright phenomenon that would be visible through instruments, if not the naked eye.

Black holes and relativity

The first modern solution of general relativity that would be able to characterise a black hole was discovered by Karl Schwarzschild in the year 1916. However, till the 1960s, black holes were thought to be a mathematical curiosity. They were something that mathematics predicted the existence of, but did not have any proof of its existence. The discovery of neutron stars generated interest in gravitationally collapsed compact objects as a possible reality in astrophysics.

Many spiral galaxies may have black holes at their centre.

The Milky Way has a massive

A black hole keeps sucking in light as well as everything that lies within its gravitational reach. ▶

A black hole at the centre with a mass 4.6 million times that of the Sun.

Observing black holes

Due to the fact that nothing escapes the field of a black hole, including light, X-rays, radio waves and other forms of electromagnetic radiation, they are very hard to detect. Black holes must be detected by their interactions with the rest of the universe. Once stabilised, they have three basic independent properties: mass, charge and angular momentum. These are also the properties that can be used to detect them externally. The simplest static black holes have only mass, but neither electric charge nor angular momentum. They are commonly referred to as Schwarzschild black holes after Karl Schwarzschild.

A diagrammatic representation of the fabric of time with a wormhole that can allow time travel faster than the speed of light. ▶

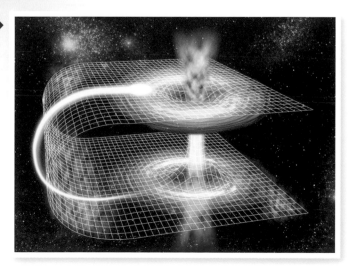

Event horizon

The appearance of an event horizon defines a black hole. This is a boundary in space-time through which both matter and light can only pass inward towards the black hole. Nothing can come out from within the event horizon, not even light. The boundary is named as an event horizon because no information about an event occurring inside this horizon will pass outside. Thus, all events within it have an information horizon.

Distorting space-time

An interesting thing about black holes is a by-product of their distortion of time and space. They tend to warp the space around them as well as cause time dilation, where time passes slower and slower as you get closer to the black hole. As a result, they may create wormholes that allow faster-than-light time travel.

FUN FACT

Did you know that you cannot see a black hole directly?

Nova

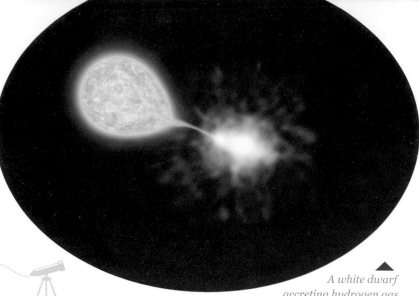

A nova and supernova are both bright events in the sky that are generally visible during the night to the naked eye. Until very recently, they were used very interchangeably. However, recent discoveries have found that the two have completely different causes.

A white dwarf accreting hydrogen gas from a red giant star that has moved too close to its orbit.

Origin

Tycho Brahe coined the term "nova" after observing the supernova SN 1572 in the constellation Cassiopeia in the sixteenth century. He described it in his book *De Stella nova*, which is Latin for "concerning the new star". It was from here that the term nova was coined, though strictly speaking, the observed event was a supernova.

Cataclysmic nuclear explosion

A nova is a cataclysmic nuclear explosion on a white dwarf. A nova is caused by the accretion of hydrogen onto the surface of the star. Due to the closeness, hydrogen accumulates on the surface of a white dwarf in a binary system, after being bled off from the larger star. It then ignites and starts nuclear fusion in a raging manner.

Mechanism

The gases are compacted on the white dwarf's surface by its intense gravity, compressed and heated to very high temperatures as additional material is drawn in. As the white dwarf is dying and composed of degenerate matter, it does not absorb the material and inflate—as another star like the Sun would.

For most binary system parameters, the hydrogen burning is thermally unstable once it has reached the required fusion temperatures. As a result, it rapidly converts a large amount of the hydrogen into other heavier elements in a runaway reaction. This liberates an enormous amount of energy, blowing the remaining gases away from the white dwarf's surface and producing an extremely bright outburst of light.

Nova Eridani 2009 as seen on the night of a full moon.

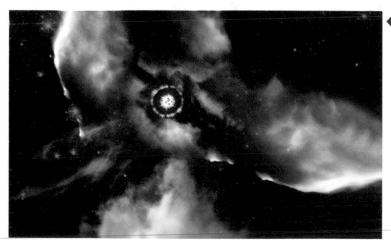

A nova as represented by an artist.

FUN FACT

Astronomers estimate that the Milky Way experiences roughly 30 to 60 novae per year. Few novae like the RS Ophiuchi recur every few decades and are relatively rare.

Supernova

A supernova is a stellar explosion that briefly outshines an entire galaxy. The amount of energy that is radiated is as much as the Sun or any ordinary star is expected to emit over its entire lifespan, but over a brief burst. The supernova fades from view over a period of weeks or months.

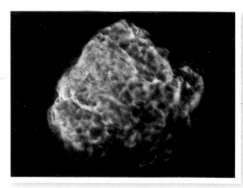

▲ *Remnants of a supernova continue to be bright for a while. Most gas clouds are formed by supernova events.*

Earliest observation and discovery

The earliest recorded supernova was SN 185, which was viewed by Chinese astronomers in 185 AD. SN 1006 is the brightest recorded supernova in human history. Earlier, supernovae were considered as a brighter form of novae. Walter Baade and Fritz Zwicky at Mount Wilson Observatory did early work on what was originally believed to be simply a new category of novae. The term "super-novae" was first used during 1931 lectures held at Caltech by this pair. The hyphen had been lost and the modern name was in use by 1938.

Rare events

Supernovae are relatively rare events within a galaxy, occurring about thrice in a century in the Milky Way. Supernovae cannot be predicted with any meaningful accuracy and must be observed in progress. Thus, both amateurs and professionals conduct extensive supernova searching. Supernova searches fall mainly into two classes: those searches focussed on relatively nearby events and those looking for explosions farther away.

Format

Supernova discoveries are reported to the IAU's Central Bureau for Astronomical Telegrams. The name of a supernova is in the following format: SN followed by the year of discovery, suffixed with a one or two-letter designation.

Classification

Supernovae are classified as follows:

Type	Average peak absolute magnitude	Approximate energy (foe)	Days to peak luminosity	Days from peak to 10% luminosity
Ia	−19	1	approx. 19	around 60
Ib/c (faint)	around −15	0.1	15–25	unknown
Ib	around −17	1	15–25	40–100
Ic	around −16	1	15–25	40–100
Ic (bright)	to −22	above 5	roughly 25	roughly 100
II-b	around −17	1	around 20	around 100
II-L	around −17	1	around 13	around 50
II-P (faint)	around −14	0.1	roughly 15	unknown
II-P	around −16	1	around 15	Plateau then around 50
IInd	around −17	1	12–30 or more	50–150
IIn (bright)	to −22	above 5	above 50	above 100

Extreme Helium Star

Most stars consist of hydrogen as their primary component. However, there are certain stars that are extremely low or almost devoid of hydrogen. This category of stars is termed as "hydrogen-deficient stars".

Hydrogen deficient stars

Cool carbon stars like R Coronae Borealis, helium-rich spectral class O or B stars, population I Wolf-Rayet stars, AM CVn stars, white dwarfs of spectral type WC and transition stars like PG 1159 are all hydrogen deficient. An extreme helium star, often abbreviated as "EH", is a low-mass supergiant that is almost devoid of hydrogen.

Discovery

Daniel M. Popper discovered the first known extreme helium star at the McDonald Observatory in Austin, USA, in 1942. By 1996, 25 possible helium stars were identified. This was further narrowed to 21 by 2006. Extreme helium stars are characterised as those that displays no lines of hydrogen in their spectrum, but strong helium lines as well as the presence of carbon and oxygen.

Size and composition

The known extreme helium stars are "supergiants". Hydrogen is less abundant by a factor of 10,000 or more,

and surface temperatures range from 9,000–35,000 K. There are two popular theories as to how these stars are formed and why they have their unique composition.

The double-degenerate (DD) model: This explains stars forming in a binary system. It has a small helium white dwarf and a more massive carbon–oxygen white dwarf. Gravity causes them to collide and form a dwarf that ignites into a supergiant.

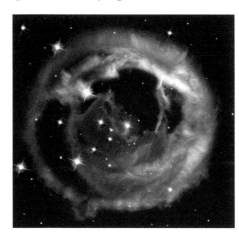

The final-flash (FF) model: It says that helium ignites in a shell around the core, causing the dwarf to rapidly expand.

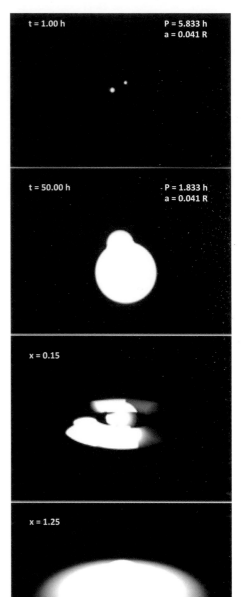

The various stages as postulated by the DD model–from the binary star to the EHe.

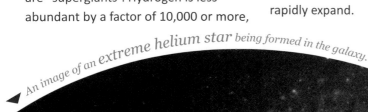

An image of an extreme helium star being formed in the galaxy.

FUN FACT

It must be noted that the composition of examined EHes matches those predicted by the DD theory.

Red Giant

 A red giant is a luminous giant star of low or intermediate mass. Its mass usually ranges between 0.3 to eight times that of our Sun. These stars are usually in a very late phase of stellar evolution. Red giants have radii tens to hundreds of times larger than that of the Sun. Their outer envelope is lower in temperature, about 5,000 K and below.

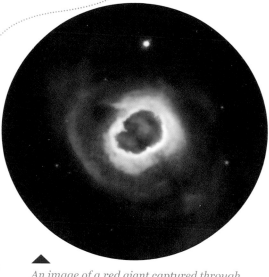

An image of a red giant captured through a thermal imaging telescope.

Formation

When a star initially forms from a collapsing molecular cloud in the interstellar medium, it primarily contains hydrogen and helium, with trace amounts of "metals", i.e., any element heavier than helium. When the star exhausts the hydrogen fuel in its core, nuclear reactions can no longer continue, and thus the core begins contracting due to its own gravity. This causes the remaining hydrogen to undergo fusion in a shell around the core at a faster rate. The outer layers of the star then expand greatly. This begins the red giant phase of a star's life.

Colour and naming

Since the expansion of the star greatly increases its surface area, red giants tend to be cooler and burn with an orange hue. Despite their name, they are closer to orange in reality. The M-type stars HD 208527, HD 220074 and K-giants including Pollux, Gamma Cephei and Iota Draconis are some examples of red giants with planets.

Life around red giants

It has traditionally been suggested that life could not evolve on planets orbiting them. However, current research suggests that there would be a habitable zone at twice the distance from Earth to Sun for a billion years. At a distance of nine AU, such a habitable zone would only exist for 100 million years. As of June 2014, 50 giant planets have been discovered around giant stars. These giants are much larger than those found around sun-sized stars.

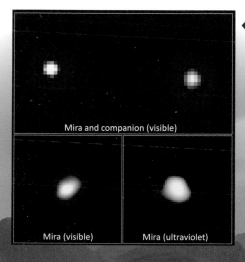

Mira and companion (visible)

Mira (visible)

Mira (ultraviolet)

The bright yellow dot in the top left corner is a star the size of the Sun. It serves as a comparison to show how big a red giant could be.

An artist's conception of a red giant at sunset on one of its orbiting worlds.

VY Canis Major

VY Canis Majoris or VY CMa is a red hypergiant star. It is located in the constellation Canis Major. It is one of the largest and brightest red hypergiants observed so far. It has a diameter of 1800 solar radii. This star emits energy very quickly and therefore, only exists for a few million years. It is estimated to be 4900 light years away from Earth. This star shows periodic light changes that last for approximately 2200 days.

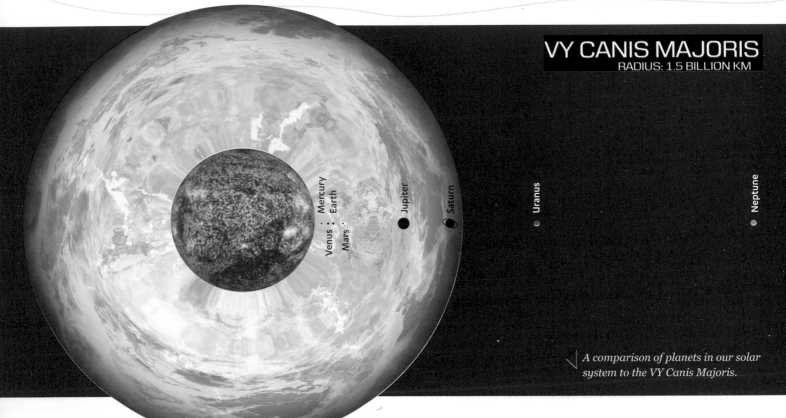

VY CANIS MAJORIS
RADIUS: 1.5 BILLION KM

Venus · Mercury Earth · Mars · Jupiter Saturn Uranus Neptune

A comparison of planets in our solar system to the VY Canis Majoris.

The crimson star

The first known recorded observation of VY Canis Majoris is in the star catalogue of Jérôme Lalande, who recorded it on 7th March, 1801. Since 1847, VY CMa has been known to be a crimson star. Originally, University of Minnesota Professor Roberta M. Humphreys approximated that the radius of VY CMa is 1800–2100 times that of the Sun. This would make it the largest known star based on its radius.

A big star

There have been conflicting opinions of the properties of VY CMa. A commonly held theory states that the star is a very large and luminous red hypergiant. However, various larger estimates of the size and luminosity fall outside the bounds of current stellar theory. In another theory, the star is a normal red supergiant, with a radius around 600 times that of our Sun.

Surface of VY CMa

This star also illustrates the conceptual problem of defining the "surface" of very large stars. This is very important for multiple reasons, including determining its radius and thus its size. It is a hundred thousand times less dense than the atmosphere of Earth (air) at sea level. Its average density is 0.000005 to 0.000010 kg per m^3. Additionally, the star is constantly losing mass at an astounding rate. The boundary of such a star is usually defined by its "Rosseland Radius", which is based on its opaqueness to light.

The brightest point is VY Canis Majoris. This is an actual image taken by the Rutherford observatory on 7th September, 2014.

Sirius

Sirius is the brightest star system in Earth's night sky. The name "Sirius" is derived from the Ancient Greek "Seirios", which means "glowing" or "scorcher". What appears to be a single star to the naked eye is actually a binary system of a white star with a faint white dwarf. This system is formally known as Alpha Canis Majoris or alpha CMa.

In this image of Sirius, Sirius B is visible as a small dot to the top right of Sirius A.

Sirius in ancient Egypt

Sirius is recorded in the earliest astronomical records. It was known in ancient Egypt as "Sopdet", which is written in Greek as "Sothis". The Egyptians based their calendar on the heliacal rising of Sirius. This heliacal rising marked the flooding of the Nile in ancient Egypt and the "dog days" of summer for the ancient Greeks.

Sirius to Polynesians

To the Polynesians in the southern hemisphere, it marked winter. The heliacal rising of Sirius refers to the day it becomes visible just before sunrise after moving far away from the glare of the Sun.

Dog star

Due to its prominent position in Canis Majoris (greater Dog) constellation, Sirius is often also referred to as the "Dog star".

Brightness

Sirius is the brightest star system in the night sky with almost twice the brightness of the second brightest star, Canopus. However, it is not as bright as the moon, Venus or Jupiter. In fact, even Mars and Mercury appear brighter than Sirius at times.

Types of Sirius

The two stars of the Sirius system are termed as Sirius A and Sirius B. Sirius A is a white main-sequence star with an estimated surface temperature of 9,940 K. It has an estimated mass which is twice that of the Sun. Sirius B is a star that has already evolved off the main sequence and transformed into a white dwarf. It has a mass almost equal to that of the Sun. It is one of the most massive white dwarfs known to us.

A Chandra X-ray observatory image of the Sirius star system.

Red, blue or white?

Greek astronomer Ptolemy had described the star of Sirius to be red in colour around 150 CE. However, poet Marcus Manilius described it as blue in his poems around 1 CE and ancient China has been describing it as white since 4 CE. Astronomers believe that this star keeps changing its colour. However, the reason is still being debated upon.

FUN FACT

The Sirius binary system is thought to be around 230 million years old.

15

Arcturus

Arcturus is the brightest star in the northern celestial hemisphere. It lies in the constellation "Bootes" and is known as "Alpha Bootes". It is the fourth brightest star in the night sky, after Sirius, Canopus and Alpha Centauri. It lies barely 36.7 light years from Earth, making it very close by celestial standards.

FUN FACT

Arcturus became famous when its light was rumoured to be the mechanism used to open the 1933 Chicago World's Fair. The star was chosen as it was thought that light from Arcturus had started its journey at about the time of the previous Chicago World's Fair in 1893. The star is 36.7 light years from Earth and the light started its journey in 1896.

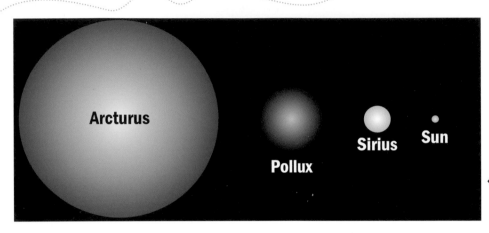

◀ An image showing the sizes of various stars, relative to one another.

Early observations

Arcturus has been significant to observers since recorded antiquity. It was linked to the God Enlil and is also known as "Shudun", meaning yoke, in ancient Mesopotamia. Ptolemy of ancient Greece described Arcturus as "subrufa" or slightly red. Prehistoric Polynesian navigators knew Arcturus as "Hōkūleʻa", the star of joy. This civilisation used Arcturus as a navigational guide. The use of Arcturus is one of the methods by which Polynesians became such fabled sailors without any instruments.

Visibility

Arcturus can be observed during the day with a telescope. French mathematician and astronomer Jean-Baptiste Morin did this in 1635, making it the first star to be seen during the day. Arcturus is a type K0 III red giant star. Visibly, it is at least 110 times brighter than the Sun. However, most of the light given off by it is infrared and not visible to the naked eye. This is because the surface is cooler than the Sun.

Binary system

It is suggested that Arcturus is actually a part of a binary star system. The secondary star seems to be about 20 times dimmer than the primary one and orbits so close to Arcturus that it is not possible as of yet to distinguish it from the main star. There have been many focussed observations undertaken for this but the results remain inconclusive.

◀ Arcturus as observed from a telescope.

An optical image of Arcturus. As evident, the brightness is clearly visible.

Betelgeuse

Betelgeuse is the ninth brightest star in the night sky and second brightest in the constellation of Orion. It is also known by its official name or Bayer designation "alpha orionis". This is often shortened to alpha-orionis or alpha ori. The star's name is derived from the Arabic Yad al-Jauzā, which means "the hand of Orion". It refers to the star's position in the Orion constellation.

Classification

The star is classified as a red supergiant. It is one of the largest and most luminous observable stars. If Betelgeuse were in the solar system in place of the Sun, its surface would extend past the asteroid belt. It would possibly extend to the orbit of Jupiter and beyond. The resulting mass would be completely engulfing Mercury, Venus, Earth and Mars. Betelgeuse has a mass estimated to be around 30 times that of the Sun.

Variable brightness

It is one of the stars with greatly varying brightness. Sir John Herschel, in *Outlines of Astronomy*, first described the variation in Betelgeuse's brightness in 1836. This makes it easy to spot and identify with the naked eye. It also has a distinctive reddish-orange colour.

Eventual fate

Its fate depends on its mass. This is a critical factor that is not well understood. The most likely scenario is that the supergiant will continue to burn and fuse elements until its core is iron, at which point Betelgeuse will explode as a type II supernova. As of 2014, the most recent theory suggests

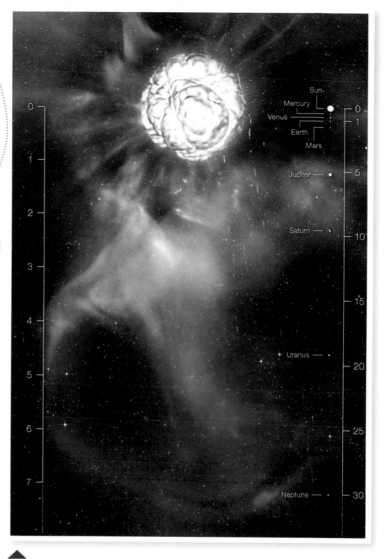

▲ *A computer generated image of Betelgeuse going supernova. The rest of the planets can be seen faintly.*

that it will explode as a supernova within 100,000 years. The event is expected to leave a neutron star 20 km in diameter.

Cultural significance

This star is popular in science fiction. The star's unusual name inspired the title of the 1988 film *Beetle juice*. It was reported that scriptwriter Michael McDowell was impressed by how many people made the connection between the film and the star. The red star Borgil in *Lord of the Rings* may also have been inspired by Betelgeuse.

◄ *A comparison between Aldebaran, Rigel, Antares and Betelgeuse.*

FUN FACT

Medieval translators misread the Arabic character for Y as B, which gave the star its current name.

Polaris

 Polaris is the brightest star in the constellation Ursa Minor and the 45th brightest star in the night sky. It is very close to the north celestial pole and is commonly used for navigation. Thus, it is also commonly known as the pole star, lodestar or guiding star.

Star system of Polaris

It is actually a multiple star system. It consists of one main star, Alpha UrsaMinoris (UMi) Aa and two smaller companions, Alpha UMi B and Alpha UMi Ab. There are also two distant components, Alpha UMi C and Alpha UMi D.

Classification and characteristics

Alpha UMi Aa is a yellow supergiant with a mass 4.5 times that of the Sun. The two smaller companions are as follows:

● **Alpha UMi B** - is a main-sequence star orbiting at a distance of 2400 AU and a mass 1.39 times that of the Sun.

● **Alpha UMi Ab** - is a very close main sequence star at a distance of 18.8 AU and a mass 1.26 times that of the Sun.

Alpha UMi Aa is visible to the naked eye and even a modest telescope can see Alpha UMi B. The system is at an approximate distance of 434 light years from Earth.

Pole star

Because Alpha UMi nearly lies in a direct line with the axis of Earth's rotation "above" the North Pole, it stands almost motionless in the sky. As a result, all the stars of the Northern sky appear to rotate around Polaris. It makes an excellent fixed point to draw measurements for celestial navigation and astrometry.

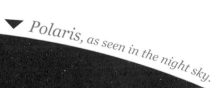

An artist's rendering of the Polaris system, based on images captured through telescopes.

A photographer's trick shot recording the movement of stars due to the rotation of Earth.

Polaris, as seen in the night sky.

FUN FACT

The celestial North Pole is not fixed. It moves due to Earth's motion. As a result, Polaris wasn't always a pole star and will not be one after a few centuries.

Alpha Centauri

Alpha Centauri is the brightest star in the southern constellation of Centaurus and the third brightest star in the night sky. It is actually a binary star system although it appears as a single object to the unaided eye. This system is located 1.34 parsecs or 4.37 light years from the Sun. This makes it the closest star system to our solar system.

Discovery

English explorer Robert Hues brought Alpha Centauri to the attention of European observers in his 1592 work *Tractatus de Globis*. He wrote, "Now, therefore, there are but three stars of the first magnitude that I could perceive in all those parts, which are never seen here in England. The first of these is that bright star in the sterne of Argo, which they call Canobus. The second is in the end of Eridanus. The third (referring to Alpha Centauri) is in the right foote of the Centaure". Argo and Canobus refer to Arcturus and Canopus, respectively. Jean Richaud first observed the binary nature of Alpha Centauri AB in December 1689. An astronomer and Jesuit priest, he made the finding incidentally while observing a passing comet from his station in Puducherry, India.

Alpha Centauri A

Alpha Centauri A is the primary member of the binary system. It is a sun-like main sequence star, but slightly larger and more luminous. It is about 1.1 times the Sun's mass with an orbit about 23 per cent greater. As an individual star, it is the fourth brightest, being slightly dimmer than Arcturus.

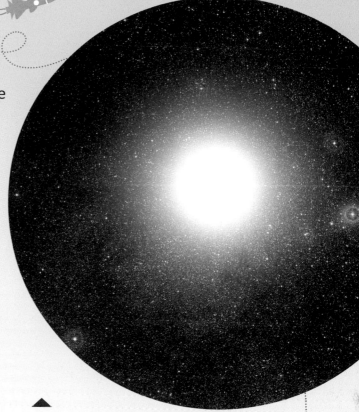

The Alpha Centauri appears as a bright star through a normal telescope.

Alpha Centauri and Beta Centauri as seen through a camera; it is impossible to distinguish the two binary stars here. ▼

Alpha Centauri B

Alpha Centauri B is the secondary member of the binary system. It is slightly smaller and less luminous than the Sun. It is mainly orange in colour, has 0.9 times the mass of the Sun and is 14 per cent smaller in radius. Without Alpha Centauri A, Alpha Centauri B would be a distant 21st brightest star in the night sky.

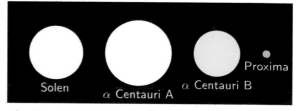

▲ *Comparision between the sizes of Solen, Alpha Centauri A, Alpha Centauri B and Proxima.*

Alpha Centauri C

Alpha Centauri C is the third star found in the proximity of Alpha Centauri A and B. It is also called Proxima. It is a much smaller star than the other two. This star could be called a part of a triple star system with the other two; however, its orbital period is too long.

Proxima Centauri

Proxima Centauri is a red dwarf that is about 4.24 light years from the Sun. It lies inside the G-cloud in the constellation of Centaurus. Scottish astronomer Robert Innes, the Director of the Union Observatory in South Africa, discovered it in 1915. It derives its name from the Latin word "proxima", meaning "close to" or "closest". This is because Proxima Centauri is the closest star to the Sun.

Star system

It is a very likely part of a triple star system with Alpha Centauri A and B. The gravitational pull of the two stars and their short distance makes this highly likely. However, its orbital period may be greater than 500,000 years. As a result, we are not sure of this fact.

Brightness

Proxima has a very low average luminosity. However, it is a flare star that undergoes random dramatic increases in brightness because of magnetic activity. When it was discovered, it was found to be the lowest-luminosity star known at the time.

Size

Being a red dwarf, it is a small star. Its radius is one-seventh and mass is only 12.3 per cent of the Sun. The star's relatively low energy-production rate suggests that it will be a main-sequence star for another four trillion years. This is nearly 300 times the current age of the universe. It is hypothesised that a life-sustaining planet could exist in orbit around it and other red dwarfs. Its habitable zone lies between 0.023 and 0.054 AU from the star. Such a planet would have an orbital period of 3.6–14 days.

A Hubble telescope image of Proxima Centauri.

Travelling to Proxima

Astronomers consider that it is possible to travel to Proxima Centauri as it is bound to pass relatively close to Earth on its orbit before moving far away again. However, it could take about thousands of years for a spacecraft from Earth to land on a planet that is orbiting this red dwarf star.

An enlarged image of the red dwarf star of Proxima Centauri.

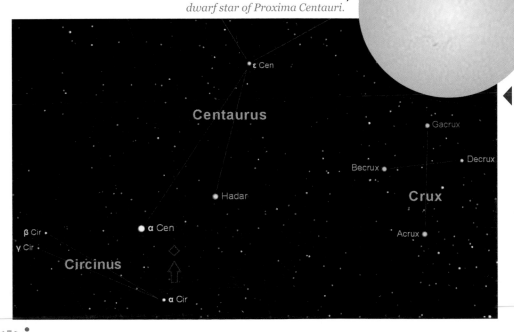

The red arrow shows the position of the Proxima Centauri.

FUN FACT

If such a planet exists, Proxima Centauri moves little in the planet's sky and most of the surface experiences either day or night perpetually.

OGLE-TR-122/123

 OGLE refers to the Optical Gravitational Lensing Experiment. It is a Polish astronomical project based at the University of Warsaw. While chiefly concerned with discovering dark matter through the use of the micro-lensing technique, it has discovered two notable and similar star systems.

Star systems

OGLE-TR-122 and OGLE-TR-123 are binary stellar systems. Each contains one of the smallest main-sequence stars, whose radius has been measured. The orbital period for OGLE-TR-122 is approximately 7.3 days. The orbital period for OGLE-TR-123 is approximately 1.8 days.

Stars of 122

The primary star for OGLE-TR-122, which is also known as OGLE-TR-122A, is thought to resemble the Sun. The smaller star, OGLE-TR-122B, is estimated to have a radius around 0.12 times that of the Sun. This means that it is only 1.2 times the radius of Jupiter. The mass of

122B is also only 10 per cent of the Sun, which makes it about 100 times more than Jupiter. OGLE-TR-122B's mass is close to the lowest possible mass for a hydrogen-fusing star. The average density of the star is approximately 50 times that of the Sun or over 80 times the density of water. The observed transit of OGLE-TR-122B provides the first direct evidence of a star with a radius comparable to Jupiter.

Stars of 123

The primary star for OGLE-TR-123, known as OGLE-TR-123A, is thought to be slightly larger than the Sun. The smaller star, OGLE-TR-123B, is estimated

Solar planets with 122B for scale. 123B is only slightly smaller than 122B in mass, but slightly greater in radius.

to have a radius around 0.13 times that of the Sun. This makes it only 1.3 times the radius of Jupiter. The mass of 123B is also only 8.5 per cent of the Sun, which makes it about 95 times more than that of Jupiter. OGLE-TR-123B's mass is close to the lowest possible mass for a hydrogen-fusing star. The threshold for hydrogen fusion is thought to be around 0.07 or 0.08 of the mass of the Sun. The observed transit of OGLE-TR-123B provides the second evidence for a star with a radius comparable to Jupiter. This allowed us additional data for calculations after 122B was first observed.

An artist's representation of OGLE-TR-123 on the horizon of alternate worlds.

Asterism

An asterism is a pattern of stars that is recognised in Earth's night sky. It may be a part of an official constellation or composed of more than one star. In most cases, asterisms are composed of stars that are visible in the same general direction, but are not physically related. They are at significantly different distances from Earth, like constellations.

Background

Right since the beginning of astronomy, it is common to cluster various stars together into connect-the-dots or stick-figure patterns. Most cultures have recognised forms or groups of stars called constellations. Constellations were informal; anyone could create a figure and call it a constellation. Clarification was necessary to determine which groupings are constellations and which stars belonged to them.

Official naming

In 1930, the IAU divided the sky into 88 official constellations with precise boundaries. Any other grouping is an asterism. However, a true star cluster, whose stars are gravitationally related, is not an asterism.

Examples

There are various prominent examples of seasonal Asterisms (as seen in the northern hemisphere).

● **Spring** — the Great Diamond consisting of Arcturus, Spica, Denebola and Cor Caroli

● **Summer** — the Summer Triangle of Deneb, Altair and Vega

Brocchi's cluster or "the coat hanger" asterism in the constellation Vulpecula as seen through binoculars.

● **Autumn** — the Great Square of Pegasus is the quadrilateral formed by the stars α Pegasi, β Pegasi, γ Pegasi and α Andromedae

● **Winter** — the Winter Hexagon formed with Sirius, Procyon and Pollux, including 2nd magnitude Castor - Capella, Aldebaran and Rigel on the periphery and Betelgeuse located off-centre

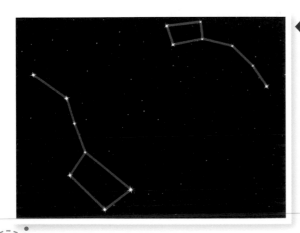

The Big Dipper or The Plough is one of the most recognisable asterisms. It is also a part of Ursa Major.

FUN FACT

Asterisms are groups of stars that have not been categorised as something else. Objects that do not fall within the bounds of this definition include the Milky Way, nebulae and open clusters.

Cygnus

Cygnus is a northern constellation lying on the plane of the Milky Way. It derives its name from the Latinised Greek word for swan. In Greek mythology, this constellation represented God Zeus's swan. It may either be the one that was taken to seduce the Spartan queen Leda or the nymph Nemesis. It is one of the most recognisable constellations of the northern summer and autumn, and was among the 48 constellations listed by Ptolemy.

A diagrammatic representation of the constellation of Cygnus; the diagram looks like a swan in flight.

Location of Cygnus

Cygnus is a very large constellation. It is bordered on the east by Lacerta, on the west by Lyra, on the south by Vulpecula, on the north and east by Cepheus, on the north and west by Draco, and on the southeast by Pegasus. A polygon of 28 segments is considered as an official constellation. Belgian astronomer Eugène Delporte set this rule in 1930. Cygnus ranks 16th of the 88 constellations when sorted by size. It covers 804 square degrees and around 1.9 per cent of the night sky.

Constituents of Cygnus

The brightest star in Cygnus is Deneb, which is the 19th brightest star in the sky. Deneb is one of the stars of the prominent asterism, the Summer Triangle along with Vega and Altair. The Milky Way runs through Cygnus.

Cygnus also contains many notable objects such as:

● Cygnus X-1 — the first known black hole

● The Cygnus Loop — a large supernova remnant

Cygnus as visible through a telescope.

● The North American Nebula — a cloud of interstellar gas shaped like a continent

● The star 61 Cygni — 11.4 light years from Earth, it is the 15th nearest star and was the first to have its distance measured and recorded

● Over hundred known planets — Cygnus is a constellation that includes stars that have over 100 known planets. This is more than the planets of the stars of any other constellations. This has been possible because the Kepler satellite had surveyed when it was looking for extrasolar planets. It contains the Kepler-11 system that has six planets all within 1° to each other.

Ursa Major

Ursa Major is a constellation that is visible throughout the year in most of the northern hemisphere. The name comes from the Latin word meaning "larger bear". It is also known as the Great Bear and Charles' Wain. It has been reconstructed as an Indo-European constellation.

Background

The constellation of Ursa Major has been seen as a bear by many distinct civilisations. It dates back to more than 13,000 years and stems from a common oral tradition. Julien d'Huy reconstructed the following Palaeolithic state of the story:

"There is a horned herbivorous animal, especially an elk. One human pursues it in the sky. The animal is alive when it is transformed into a constellation, forming the Big Dipper".

This story was created to support the idea of Ursa Major's origins. It was one of the 48 constellations listed by the second century CE astronomer Ptolemy.

In literature

The Ursa Major is also prominent in literature. Poets such as Homer, Spencer, Shakespeare and Tennyson mention it in their work. The Finnish epic "Kalevala" has references to Ursa Major.

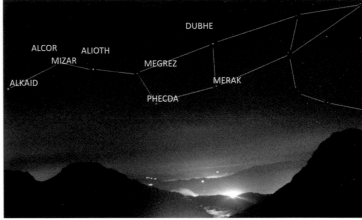

▲ *A star map of Ursa Major.*

Constituents of Ursa Major

The constellation consists of one major asterism and seven distinct stars. They are as follows:

1. The "Big Dipper" (or plough) asterism. It is made up of seven bright stars that together comprise one of the best-known patterns in the sky.

2. Alpha Ursae Majoris, also known by the Arabic name "Dubhe" (the bear). It is the 35th brightest star in the sky and the second brightest of Ursa Major.

3. Beta Ursae Majoris, called "Merak", which is Arabic for "the loins of the bear".

4. Gamma Ursae Majoris or "Phecda" (thigh).

5. Delta Ursae Majoris or "Megrez" (root of the tail).

6. Epsilon Ursae Majoris, known as "Alioth". This name does not refer to a bear, but to a "black horse". Alioth is the brightest star of Ursa Major and the 33rd brightest star in the sky.

7. Zeta Ursae Majoris, "Mizar", is the second star at the end of the handle of the Big Dipper and the constellation's 4th brightest star. Mizar means girdle in Arabic.

8. Eta Ursae Majoris, known as either "Alkaid" or "Benetnash", meaning the "end of the tail". Alkaid is the 3rd brightest star of Ursa Major.

A diagrammatic representation of the constellation of the Great bear; the diagram looks like a bear standing on two legs.

Orion

Orion is a prominent constellation that is located on the celestial equator. It is visible throughout the world and is one of the most conspicuous and recognisable constellations in the night sky. It was named after a hunter in Greek mythology.

Background in different cultures

Orion has been observed from antiquity and finds a mention in the astronomy of the following regional cultures:

- Ancient Near East
- Greco-Roman antiquity
- Middle East
- East Asian antiquity
- European folklore
- Americas

Constituents of Orion

The brightest and most important seven stars in Orion are as follows:

1. Betelgeuse, or Alpha Orionis, is a massive M-type red supergiant star nearing the end of its life. It is the second brightest star in Orion, and is a semi-regular variable star and the 8th brightest star in the night sky. It forms the right shoulder of Orion.

2. Rigel, also known as Beta Orionis, is a B-type, blue supergiant that is the 6th brightest star in the night sky. It serves as the left foot of Orion, the hunter.

3. Bellatrix or Gamma Orionis is colloquially known as the "Amazon Star". It is the 27th brightest star in the night sky. Bellatrix is considered to be a B-type blue giant. It serves as Orion's left shoulder.

4. Mintaka, also known as Delta Orionis, is the faintest of the three stars in Orion's Belt. It is a multiple star system, composed of a large B-type blue giant and a more massive O-type white star. It is located in the Orion's Belt.

5. Alnilam is also called Epsilon Orionis. Also called Al Nathin, Alnilam is named for the Arabic phrase meaning "string of pearls". Alnilam is a B-type blue supergiant. Despite being nearly twice as far from the Sun as Mintaka and Alnitak, the other two belt stars, its luminosity makes it nearly equal in magnitude.

6. Alnitak, meaning "the girdle", is also called Zeta Orionis. It is the easternmost star in Orion's Belt. It is a triple star some 800 light years away. The primary star of Alnitak is a blue supergiant and the brightest class O star in the night sky.

7. Saiph is also called Kappa Orionis. It serves as Orion's right foot. Saiph is of a similar distance and size to Rigel, but appears much fainter.

An Orion constellation map with details of the stars and their relative placements.

Nakshatra

Nakshatra or náksatra is the term for lunar mansion in Hindu astrology. A nakshatra is one of 27 (sometimes also 28) sectors along the ecliptic. These are named after the most prominent asterisms in the respective sectors.

Origin and background

Nakshatras are often referred to as Hindu constellations, though their distinctive name is more commonly used. Originally, in Vedic Sanskrit, the term nákṣatra may refer to any heavenly body or to "the stars" collectively. The classical sense of "lunar mansion" is first found in the Atharvaveda. This later evolved into the primary meaning of the term in Classical Sanskrit.

The starting point

The starting point for the nakshatras is that on the ecliptic, which is directly opposite to the star Spica, called Chitrā in Sanskrit. The ecliptic is divided into each of the nakshatras eastwards starting from this point. The number of nakshatras reflects the number of days in a lunar month. The modern period of a lunar month is 27.32 days. Thus, the moon traverses the width of a nakshatra in about one day. Each nakshatra is further subdivided into four quarters (or padas).

Nakshatras and their symbols

1. Ashwini — the horse's head
2. Pushya — cow's udder, lotus, arrow and a circle
3. Swati — young sprout swaying in the wind, coral
4. Shravana — ear, three footprints in an uneven row
5. Bharani — Yoni, the female reproductive organ
6. Ashlesha — serpent, a coiled snake
7. Vishaka — triumphant arch, potter's wheel
8. Dhanishta — drum, flute
9. Krittika — Agni, god of fire
10. Magha — royal throne
11. Anurada — triumphant arch, lotus
12. Shatabhishak — empty circle, thousand flowers, stars
13. Rohini — chariot, temple, banyan tree
14. Purva Phalguni — bed, hammock, fig tree
15. Jyeshta — amulet, umbrella, earring
16. Purva Bhadrapada — sword, funeral cot, man with two faces
17. Mrigashira — deer's head
18. Uttara Phalguni — bed, hammock
19. Mula — bunch of roots, elephant god
20. Uttara Bhadrapada — twins, funeral cot, snake in water
21. Ardra — teardrop, diamond, human head
22. Hasta — hand, fist
23. Purva Ashadha — elephant tusk, fan, winnowing basket
24. Revati — pair of fish, drum
25. Punarvasu — bow and quiver
26. Chitra — bright jewel, pearl
27. Uttara Ashadha — elephant tusk, small cot, planks of bed

List of nakshatras with stars

This is a list of the nakshatras with the modern stars that are most commonly associated with them. As we can see, some of the nakshatras are repeated over multiple asterisms.

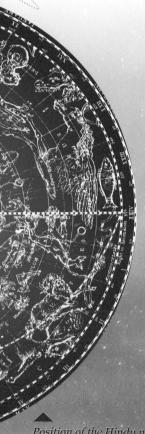

Position of the Hindu nakshatra "Mandala" as per the co-ordinates specified in Surya Siddhantha. This image shows the nakshatras overlaid on classical Greco-Roman constellations for clarity of position.

No.	Name	Associated stars
1	Ashvini - "wife of the Ashvins"	β and γ Arietis
2; 7	Bharani - "the bearer"	35, 39, and 41 Arietis
3	Krittika - an old name of the Pleiades; personified as the nurses of Kārttikeya, a son of Shiva	Pleiades
4; 9	Rohini - "the red one", a name of Aldebaran, also known asbrāhmī	Aldebaran
5; 3	Mrigashīrsha - "the deer's head", also known as āgrahāyaṇī	λ, φ Orionis
6; 4	Ardra - "the moist one"	Betelgeuse
7; 5	Punarvasu (dual) - "the two restorers of goods", also known as yamakau - "the two chariots"	Castor and Pollux
8; 6	Pushya - "the nourisher", also known as sidhya or tiṣya	γ, δ and θ Cancri
9; 7	Āshleshā - "the embrace"	δ, ε, η, ρ, and σ Hydrae
10; 15	Maghā - "the bountiful"	Regulus
11	PūrvaPhalgunī - "first reddish one"	δ and θ Leonis
12	UttaraPhalgunī - "second reddish one"	Denebola
13	Hasta - "the hand"	α, β, γ, δ and ε Corvi
14	Chitra - "the bright one", a name of Spica	Spica
15	Svāti - "Su-Ati" (sanskrit), Arcturus's name	Arcturus
16; 14	Visakha - "forked, having branches", also known as rādhā "the gift"	α, β, γ and ι Librae
17	Anuradha - "following rādhā"	β, δ and π Scorpionis
18; 16	Jyeshtha - "the eldest, most excellent"	α, σ, and τ Scorpionis
19; 17	Mula - "the root"	ε, ζ, η, θ, ι, κ, λ, μ and ν Scorpionis
20; 18	PurvaAshadha - "first of the aṣādhā", aṣādhā – "the invincible one", the name of a constellation	δ and ε Sagittarii
21	Uttara Ashadha - "second of the aṣādhā"	ζ and σ Sagittarii
22; 20	Abhijit - "victorious"	α, ε and ζ Lyrae - Vega
23; 20	Sravana	α, β and γ Aquilae
24; 21; 23	Dhanishta - "most famous", also Shravishthā "swiftest"	α to δ Delphini
24; 22	Shatabhisha - "Comprising a hundred physicians"	γ Aquarii
25; 3	PurvaBhadrapada - "the first of the blessed feet"	α and β Pegasi
26; 4	UttaraBhādrapadā - "the second of the blessed feet"	γ Pegasi and αAndromedae
27; 5	Revati - "prosperous"	ζ Piscium

Zodiac

The zodiac is a circle having 12 divisions of 30° each that are centred upon the ecliptic. The ecliptic refers to a circle on the celestial sphere that represents the Sun's path during the year. Zodiac is a term that is common in both astrology and historical astronomy.

Construction and significance

These 12 divisions are called signs. The zodiac is essentially a celestial co-ordinate system. Specifically, it is an ecliptic co-ordinate system, as opposed to an equatorial one. In the zodiac, the ecliptic is the origin of latitude. It is also the position of the Sun at vernal equinox as the origin of longitude. The vernal equinox refers to the spring equinox, which is the opposite in each hemisphere of Earth.

Etymology

The term zodiac is derived from the Latin word "zōdiacus". Zodiacus, in turn, comes from the Greek word "zōdiakoskyklos". The term means "circle of animals". It stems from the fact that half the signs of the classical Greek zodiac are represented as animals.

Comparison across cultures

The zodiac constellations have been referred to by different names over the ages. We currently use the Latin names most predominantly. Below is a table that compares the different names of the zodiac:

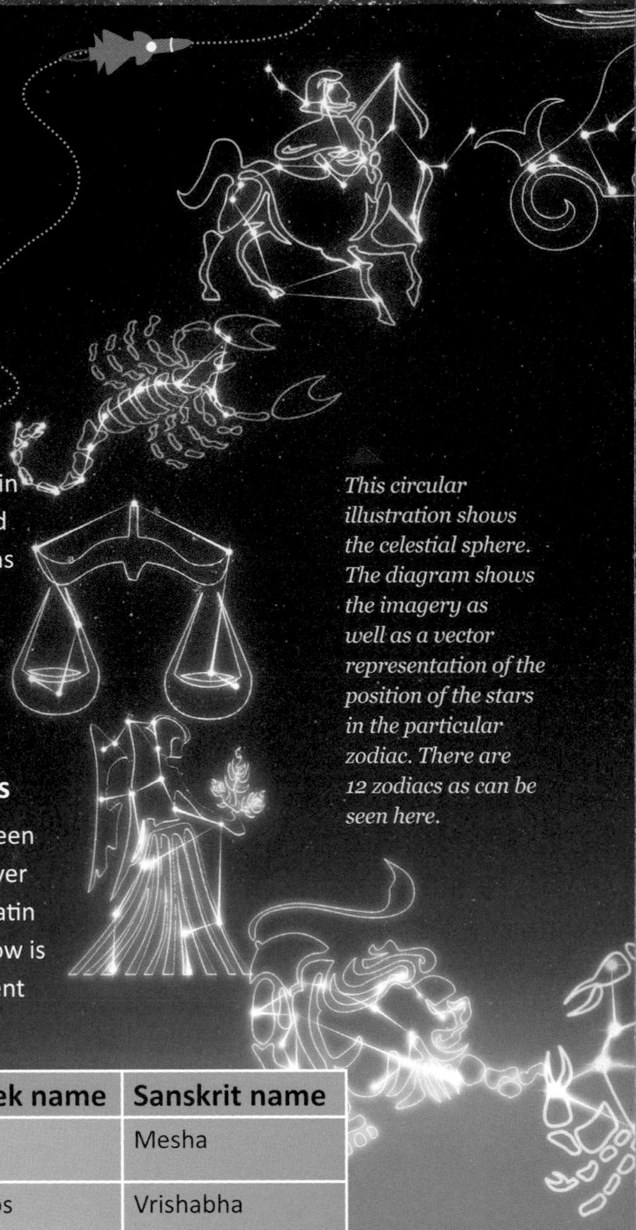

This circular illustration shows the celestial sphere. The diagram shows the imagery as well as a vector representation of the position of the stars in the particular zodiac. There are 12 zodiacs as can be seen here.

No.	Symbol	Long.	Latin name	English translation	Greek name	Sanskrit name
1	♈	0°	Aries	The ram	Krios	Mesha
2	♉	30°	Taurus	The bull	Tavros	Vrishabha
3	♊	60°	Gemini	The twins	Didymoi	Mithuna
4	♋	90°	Cancer	The crab	Karkinos	Karkata
5	♌	120°	Leo	The lion	Leōn	Simha
6	♍	150°	Virgo	The maiden	Parthenos	Kanyā
7	♎	180°	Libra	The scales	Zygos	Tulā
8	♏	210°	Scorpio	The scorpion	Skorpios	Vrśhchika
9	♐	240°	Sagittarius	The (centaur)archer	Toxotēs	Dhanusha
10	♑	270°	Capricorn	"Goat-horned" (the sea-goat)	Aigokerōs	Makara
11	♒	300°	Aquarius	The water-bearer	Hydrokhoos	Kumbha
12	♓	330°	Pisces	The fish	Ikhthyes	Mīna

Differences from astrology

Unlike the zodiac signs in astrology, which are all 30° in length, the astronomical constellations vary widely in size. Due to the constellations not being evenly distributed according to size, the Sun takes a different amount of time in each constellation.

Sun's relation to the Zodiac

Below is a table that details the Sun and its relation to the various zodiac signs. This is a sample using 2011 as a reference. There are minor changes from year to year, due to the nature of Earth's rotation and orbit.

Zodiac today

The zodiac remains the basis of the ecliptic coordinate system that is used in astronomy. However, the term and names of the 12 signs are today mostly associated with horoscopic astrology. Horoscopic astrology is the belief that the constellation in which the Sun is at the time of one's birth somehow determines the traits and future of a person. Along with the Sun, the position of the moon in the zodiac is also used for both astrology and astronomy. However, the moon moves through the ecliptic very quickly, finishing the 360° arc in a little over 27 days.

Constellation			
Name	**IAU boundaries**	**Solar stay**	**Brightest star**
Aries	19 April–13 May	25 days	Hamal
Taurus	14 May–19 June	37 days	Aldebaran
Gemini	20 June–20 July	31 days	Pollux
Cancer	21 July–9 August	20 days	Al Tarf
Leo	10 August–15 September	37 days	Regulus
Virgo	16 September–30 October	45 days	Spica
Libra	31 October–22 November	23 days	Zubeneschamali
Scorpius	23 November–29 November	7 days	Antares
Ophiuchus	30 November–17 December	18 days	Rasalhague
Sagittarius	18 December–18 January	32 days	KausAustralis
Capricornus	19 January–15 February	28 days	DenebAlgedi
Aquarius	16 February–11 March	24 days	Sadalsuud
Pisces	12 March–18 April	38 days	Eta Piscium

An ancient artifact marking the 12 animals around a dial at the correct longitudinal degree that they adhere to.

Leo

Leo is one of the constellations of the zodiac, lying between Cancer to the west and Virgo to the east. It is easily recognisable, as it contains many bright stars and a distinctive shape that is reminiscent of the crouching lion. Its name is Latin for lion. It is named after the Nemean lion killed by the mythical Greek hero Heracles.

A lion, the animal that represents the zodiac of Leo.

Leo as seen in the night sky.

Leo's stars

It remains as one of the 88 modern constellations today. It was also one of the 48 constellations described by the second century astronomer, Ptolemy. Leo has many bright stars. The most prominent ones are listed below:

● **Regulus:** It is designated as Alpha Leonis; it is a blue-white, main-sequence star that is located 77.5 light years from Earth. It is a double star, visible through binoculars. The traditional name of the star, Regulus, means "the little king".

● **Beta Leonis:** It is commonly called Denebola and is at the opposite end of the constellation to Regulus. It is a blue-white star that is 36 light years from Earth. Denebola means "the lion's tail".

● **Algieba:** Formally known as Gamma Leonis, it is a binary star with a third optical component. The primary and secondary ones are distinguishable in small telescopes, while the tertiary is visible through binoculars. The primary is a gold-yellow giant star and the secondary is similar, but less bright. They are 126 light years from Earth. The tertiary is unrelated and called 40 Leonis. It is a yellow-tinged star. Its traditional name, Algieba, means "the forehead".

● **Delta Leonis:** It is commonly called "Zosma". It is a blue-white star, 58 light years from Earth.

● **Epsilon Leonis:** It is a yellow giant that is 251 light years from Earth.

● **Zeta Leonis:** It is commonly called Adhafera. It is an optical triple star, the brightest and only star designated as Zeta Leonis. It is a white giant star that is 260 light years from Earth. The second brightest star, named 39 Leonis, is widely spaced to the south. The 35 Leonis is to the north and the third star in the trifecta.

● **Iota Leonis:** It is a binary star that is visible through medium-sized amateur telescopes. To the unaided eye, Iota Leonis appears to be a yellow-tinged star. The binary system is 79 light years from Earth.

● **Tau Leonis:** It is a double star that is visible through binoculars. The primary is a yellow giant star that is 621 light years from Earth.

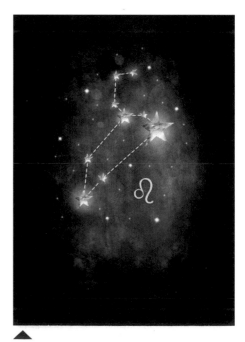

A diagrammatic representation of the stars that are present in the Leo constellation.

Scorpius

Scorpius is one of the constellations of the zodiac. It is Latin for scorpion and the constellation is sometimes known as Scorpio. It is a large constellation that is located in the southern hemisphere near the centre of the Milky Way. It lies between Libra to the west and Sagittarius to the east.

A scorpion, the reptile that represents the zodiac of Scorpius. ▶

The stars connect to show the shape of a scorpion. ◀

Background and history

The Babylonians called this constellation MUL.GIR.TAB, which is Babylonian for "Scorpion". The name can be literally interpreted as "the (creature with a) burning sting". The Javanese people of Indonesia call this constellation "Banyakangrem", which means "the brooded swan", or Kalapa Doyong, meaning "leaning coconut tree". This is due to the shape similarity. It is astronomically shortened to "Sco" in modern usage.

● Beta 1 Sco is commonly called Graffias or Acrab. It is an optical triple star.

● Delta Sco is commonly called Dschubba that means "the front".

● Theta Sco is commonly called Sargas. The origin of its name is unknown.

● Nu Sco is commonly called Jabbah.

● Epsilon Sco is commonly called Girtab, which means "the scorpion".

● PiSco is commonly called Iclil.

● Sigma Sco is commonly called Alniyat.

● Tau Sco is commonly called and also known as Alniyat. It means "the arteries" and refers to both Tau and Sigma Sco.

● Lambda Sco, commonly called Shaula, Upsilon Sco and Lesath, form the

▲ *A diagrammatic representation of the stars that are present in the Scorpius constellation.*

Scorpion's curved tail. These names have a common origin and mean "sting". λ Sco and υ Sco are sometimes referred to as the cat's eyes due to their close proximity.

Constituents of Scorpius

It contains many bright stars. The major ones are listed below:

● Antares is formally known as alpha Scorpio and "rival of Mars". The title was conferred because of its distinct reddish hue.

▼ *Scorpius as seen in the night sky.*

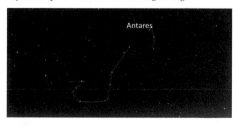

FUN FACT

The star once designated Gamma Sco is today known as "Sigma Librae". It was originally misnamed as it is well within the boundaries of Libra.

Gemini

Gemini is one of the constellations of the zodiac. It derives its name from a Latin word, meaning "twins". It is associated with the twins Castor and Pollux in Greek mythology. It was one of the 48 constellations described by Ptolemy. It remains one of the 88 modern constellations defined by the IAU today.

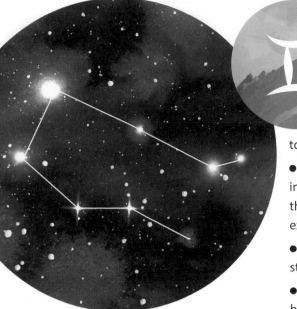

The stars connect to show the shape of twins.

Twins, Castor and Pollux represent the zodiac of Gemini.

History and background

In Meteorologica, Aristotle mentions that he observed Jupiter in conjunction with a star, and then occulting one in Gemini. This is the first such recorded observation in human history and probably occurred in 337 BCE. In 1930, Clyde Tombaugh discovered Pluto when he exposed a series of photographic plates centred on Delta Gemini.

Constituents of Gemini

It contains 85 stars that are visible from Earth without a telescope. Pollux is the brightest star in Gemini followed by Castor. Castor's designation as Alpha Gem (Gemini) is, thus, mistaken. The list of stars in Gemini is as follows:

● α Gem (Castor) — Castor is a sextuple star system that is 52 light years from Earth, which appears as a blue-white star

to the unaided eye.

● β Gem (Pollux) — The brightest star in Gemini is an orange-hued giant star that is 34 light years from Earth. An extrasolar planet revolves around it.

● γ Gem (Alhena) — It is a blue-white star that is 105 light years from Earth.

● δ Gem (Wasat) — It is a long-period binary star that is 59 light years away from Earth.

● ε Gem (Mebsuta) — A double star, the primary is a yellow supergiant that is 900 light years from Earth. The optical companion is visible through binoculars and small telescopes.

● ζ Gem (Mekbuda) — It is a double star. The primary is a yellow supergiant that is 1200 light years from Earth. It has a radius that is 60 times the Sun, making it approximately 220,000 times the size of the Sun.

● η Gem — A binary star that is 350 light years away is only distinguishable in large amateur telescopes. The primary is a semi-regular red giant.

● κ Gem — Binary star that is 143 light years from Earth. The primary is a yellow giant.

● ν Gem — It is a double star that is

visible when using binoculars and small amateur telescopes. The primary is a blue giant.

● 38 Gem — It is a binary star that is 91 light years from Earth. The primary is a white star and the secondary a yellow star.

● U Gem — It is a dwarf nova-type cataclysmic variable.

A diagrammatic representation of the stars that are present in the Gemini constellation.